D1195297

PORTALS TO READING

Reading Skills Through Literature

PARENT-TEACHER COLLECTION

THE LION, THE WITCH AND THE WARDROBE

C. S. Lewis

Reproducible Activity Book
by
Claudia Dutcher Tillman

A Note from the Author

The activities in this workbook will introduce students to the time-tested literature that should be an important part of the reading program in every school. The activities will provide students from grades four through eight with meaningful reading experiences and, at the same time, reinforce a wide variety of reading skills.

Clearly, such literary matters as style and flavor may be experienced only by reading the primary source—the book itself. So, obviously, reading the book is the student's first responsibility. Students should be reminded frequently that the workbook activities are no substitute for the original text.

Rather, the workbook activities have been designed to encourage the student to read the original text—that is, the actual words of the author. These motivating workbook activities are often based on sentences and paragraphs especially written to support the teaching objective of each workbook lesson. Thus, I have declined to tinker with the words of the author and leave them properly where they belong—in their pure form in the pages of the novel.

—Claudia Dutcher Tillman

Table of Contents

Word Attack Skills

Comprehension Skills

Study Skills

Creative Skills

Author! Author!
C. S. LEWIS

C. (Clive) S. (Staples) Lewis was born in Belfast, Northern Ireland, in November 1898. His father was a lawyer. His mother was the daughter of a naval chaplain.

Lewis' mother died when he was a young boy, and he spent most of his childhood in boarding schools.

Lewis entered Oxford University in 1917, but soon enlisted in the British Army. He was a second lieutenant and served in France during World War I. Lewis returned to Oxford and later was a tutor at Magdalen College.

Lewis has written more than thirty books including literary and religious commentaries, science fiction, and children's novels. His first book for children, *The Lion, the Witch and the Wardrobe*, was published in 1950.

Lewis wrote six more children's books, all of them about the fantasy land of Narnia. One of those books, *The Last Battle*, received the Carnegie Medal in 1957.

C. S. Lewis died in 1963.

The Story in Brief

The Lion, the Witch and the Wardrobe is set in the mysterious land of Narnia. The principal characters are two brothers, Peter and Edmund, and their sisters, Susan and Lucy.

Lucy is the one who first discovers Narnia, a magic land on the other side of an old wardrobe. Narnia lies under the curse of the evil White Witch. In Narnia, where the land is plagued by endless winter, Lucy is befriended by a Faun. The Faun helps Lucy find her way back home.

Edmund also enters Narnia through the wardrobe. He meets the evil Witch and promises to deliver his brother and sisters.

Peter and Susan soon follow Lucy and Edmund into Narnia. The children meet Mr. and Mrs. Beaver. The Beavers tell the children that the Witch's enemy, the mighty and holy lion Aslan, is returning to Narnia.

Edmund sneaks away to the Witch's castle to tell her of Aslan's return. The beavers, who know the Witch will kill any human, lead the other children to meet Aslan.

Aslan's return brings spring back to Narnia. The powerful lion continues his war on the Witch by organizing an army to free Edmund. As payment for Edmund's release, Aslan gives himself up to the Witch. The Witch kills Aslan, but because of a "Deeper Magic," Aslan comes back to life.

Aslan rescues all the creatures who have been turned to stone by the Witch. He then leads his followers into battle against the Witch's forces. The Witch is killed, and the four children become Kings and Queens of Narnia.

The children grow to adults and rule Narnia for many years. Finally, they stumble through the wardrobe back into their own world where they become children once again.

Name _____

Lucy Looks into a Wardrobe

Changing Short Vowels

Read each sentence. Then look at the word that comes after each sentence. Change the vowel in the word to form a new word that will make sense in the sentence. Write the new word on the blank in the sentence.

Example: The professor was a very old _man_ . men

1. The house was _____ miles from a railway station.   tan

2. The old house was very _____ .   beg

3. The man was so _____ that Lucy was a bit afraid.   add

4. The children did not want to go to _____ .   bad

5. Susan thought _____ lived in the woods.   fixes

6. The dining hall was a long walk _____ the hall.   dawn

7. Lucy did not want to _____ herself in the wardrobe.   shot

8. Lucy liked the _____ and feel of the fur coats.   small

9. She expected to feel the back of the wardrobe against the _____ of her fingers.   tops

10. Lucy felt something cold, soft, and wet _____ on her.   fell

11. She looked _____ over her shoulder.   buck

12. Lucy wondered why a _____ stood in the middle of the forest.   lump

13. The Faun _____ his parcels.   dripped

14. The Faun _____ an umbrella over his head.   hold

15. He _____ walking when he saw Lucy.   stepped

THE LION, THE WITCH AND THE WARDROBE

Supplying Long Vowels

One word in each of the following sentences is missing a vowel. Read each sentence. Put a vowel in each blank to form a word that will make sense in the sentence.

Example: The children's n _a_ mes were Peter, Susan, Edmund, and Lucy.

1. The old professor had no w ____ fe.

2. Hair grew all over his f ____ ce.

3. A little str ____ am ran through the garden.

4. The room was empty except for a h ____ ge wooden wardrobe.

5. Many long fur c ____ ats hung in the wardrobe.

6. Lucy opened the heavy door with ____ ase.

7. The children hoped the r ____ in would stop.

8. The c ____ ld, wet snow fell on Lucy.

9. Lucy could still see a dim l ____ ght from the open door.

10. The children l ____ ked the professor almost at once.

11. Peter believed ____ agles might live in the woods.

12. Lucy found herself in a str ____ nge new place.

13. The professor's hair was shaggy and wh ____ te.

14. Lucy walked carefully through the wet sn ____ w.

15. The Faun looked like a man from the w ____ ist up.

What Lucy Found There

Making Compounds

Two words combined form a compound. Each word in Box A forms the first part of a compound. Each word in Box B forms the second part. In the blank in each sentence below, write the compound that best completes the sentence. Use a word from each box to make your compounds.

Box A	
bed	tea
hall	day
summer	mid
ward	book
some	mantel
~~fire~~	

Box B	
time	light
shelf	kettle
robe	~~place~~
piece	room
night	way
thing	

Example: A warm blaze burned brightly in the Faun's *fireplace* .

1. Though it was _____ in Lucy's world, it was winter in Narnia.

2. Above the _____ hung a picture of an old Faun.

3. In one corner of the cave was a door that probably led to the Faun's _____ .

4. Against one wall stood a _____ full of interesting volumes.

5. The Faun put the _____ on to boil.

(continued)

Making Compounds

What Lucy Found There

6. Lucy ran toward the patch of _____ .

7. The Faun looked as though he had said _____ he had not intended.

8. The Faun told Lucy about the _____ dances in the woods.

9. Lucy jumped out of the _____ into the empty room.

10. Lucy could hear voices in the _____ .

What Lucy Found There

Finding Base Words

Each word below has been formed by adding a suffix such as *ly*, *ed*, or *ing* to a base word. On the blank beside each word, write the base word.

Example: picking *pick* _____

1. puzzled _____
2. eastern _____
3. countries _____
4. delighted _____
5. understanding _____
6. suddenly _____
7. setting _____
8. lived _____
9. gloomy _____
10. wonderful _____

11. shaking _____
12. sorrowful _____
13. covered _____
14. merely _____
15. beginning _____
16. taken _____
17. beautiful _____
18. presently _____
19. frighten _____
20. sobbing _____

Listening for Syllables

Say each of the words listed below to yourself. The number of vowel sounds you hear in each word will be the same as the number of syllables. Decide how many syllables are in each word. Then write the number on the blank after each word.

Example: wardrobe __*2*__

1. human   _____
2. excuse   _____
3. inquisitive   _____
4. reply   _____
5. understanding   _____
6. intended   _____
7. pleased   _____
8. geography   _____
9. doubt   _____
10. introduce   _____
11. creature   _____
12. almost   _____
13. through   _____
14. wondering   _____
15. sardines   _____

16. umbrella   _____
17. castle   _____
18. crunching   _____
19. stooped   _____
20. began   _____
21. popular   _____
22. midnight   _____
23. handkerchief   _____
24. ashamed   _____
25. presently   _____
26. kidnapper   _____
27. innocent   _____
28. pretty   _____
29. asked   _____
30. horrid   _____

THE LION, THE WITCH AND THE WARDROBE

Classifying Word Groups

Read the following sentences. Decide if the italicized part of the sentence tells you *where*, *when*, or *how*. Underline the correct choice.

Example: Lucy ran *into the empty hallway*.   <u>where</u>   when   how

1. Susan said they left the room *a few minutes ago*.   where   when   how

2. Lucy ran *excitedly* back to the wardrobe.   where   when   how

3. The children looked *in the wardrobe*.   where   when   how

4. Susan *carefully* pulled back the fur coats.   where   when   how

5. Peter rapped *on the wooden door*.   where   when   how

6. Edmund asked Lucy if she found new countries *in other cupboards*, too.   where   when   how

7. *That afternoon*, the children played hide-and-seek.   where   when   how

8. The children played *outdoors* during good weather.   where   when   how

9. Edmund groped *wildly* in every direction.   where   when   how

0. The snow was crisp *under his feet*.   where   when   how

(continued)

Classifying Word Groups

Edmund and the Wardrobe

11. He expected to find Lucy *soon*.	where	when	how
12. Snow lay *on the branches* of the trees.	where	when	how
13. Everything in the country was *perfectly* still.	where	when	how
14. *Just then* Edmund heard the sound of bells.	where	when	how
15. Snow fell *silently* over the countryside.	where	when	how
16. He looked *behind some trees* for Lucy.	where	when	how
17. A lady sat on a high seat *in the sledge*.	where	when	how
18. It was early morning *in this strange place*.	where	when	how
19. The lady spoke *loudly* to the dwarf.	where	when	how
20. Edmund answered the queen rather *awkwardly*.	where	when	how

THE LION, THE WITCH AND THE WARDROBE

Turkish Delight

Classifying Words

In each group of words below, one word does not belong with the others. Draw a line through the word that does not belong.

Example: silly   foolish   ~~sad~~   funny

1. minute   first   hour   day

2. wardrobe   cupboard   drawer   full

3. coat   mittens   door   scarf

4. rock   bird   squirrel   pony

5. Lucy   Narnia   Peter   Susan

6. Dwarf   Queen   Aslan   Faun

7. pie   tea   cocoa   coffee

8. excited   afraid   sad   ahead

9. nose   nest   eye   mouth

10. house   afternoon   night   evening

11. leaf   limb   light   branch

12. silence   quiet   still   notice

13. white   clouds   blue   red

14. ice   snow   golden   frost

15. fur   reindeer   bear   fox

16. knee   foot   walk   toe

17. big   sunrise   huge   large

18. hood   cap   hat   tassel

19. smell   touch   shadow   taste

20. red   run   hike   walk

Name _____

Turkish Delight

Following Directions

Below is a drawing of the path Edmund was to follow to reach the Witch's castle. Carefully read the paragraphs at the bottom of the page. Study the drawing, then locate each place underlined in the paragraphs. Write the name of each place on the correct blank.

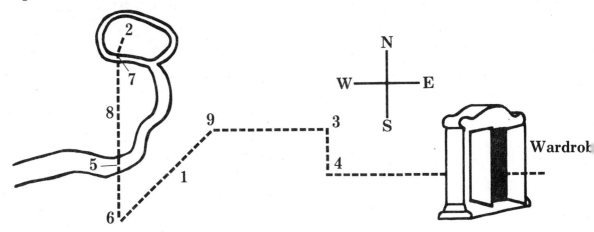

The Witch gave Edmund these directions to her house. "When you step out of the wardrobe, walk straight westward until you pass a row of <u>bushes</u>. Then turn north and continue walking. When you reach a small frozen <u>pond</u>, go west until you reach the <u>lamp-post</u>.

"At the lamp-post, go <u>southwest</u> past a small <u>woods.</u> Turn north when you reach a large <u>hill</u>. You will see a river. Cross the <u>bridge</u> over the river.

"Halfway between the bridge and the castle, you will discover some old <u>ruins</u>. Keep walking north past the ruins until you reach my moat. Cross the <u>moat bridge</u> and announce yourself. And do bring your brothers and sisters with you!"

1. _____

2. _____

3. _____

4. _____

5. _____

6. _____

7. _____

8. _____

9. _____

THE LION, THE WITCH AND THE WARDROBE

Turkish Delight

Remembering Details

The following questions are about some of the characters and events in the book. Write the answers on the lines after the questions. Be sure to use complete sentences.

1. What did the Queen wrap around Edmund to keep him warm? _____

_____

2. What was in the jewelled cup? _____

_____

3. What did the Queen ask Edmund to bring her? _____

_____

4. What did the Queen tell Edmund he would become? _____

_____

5. Where was Edmund to bring his brother and sisters? _____

_____

6. Whom did Lucy eat lunch with? _____

_____

7. What did the White Witch call herself? _____

_____

8. Why did Edmund feel uncomfortable? _____

_____

Back on This Side of the Door

Sequencing Events

The events listed below are arranged in incorrect sequence. Write *1* in the blank before the event that happened first, *2* before the event that happened next, and so on.

_____ Peter told Edmund to stop being mean to Lucy.

_____ Mrs. Macready brought some sightseers upstairs to see the house.

_____ Peter held the wardrobe door closed.

_____ Lucy said Edmund had been to Narnia.

_____ Peter and Susan talked to the Professor about Lucy.

_____ The children ran into the room with the wardrobe to escape the sightseers.

_____ Edmund said Lucy lied about the country in the wardrobe.

_____ The Professor said Lucy was not crazy.

_____ The children hid in the wardrobe.

Back on This Side of the Door

Getting the Main Idea

Read each of the following paragraphs. Then read the four sentences below each paragraph. Choose the sentence that best states the main idea of the paragraph. Then neatly copy that sentence on the line provided.

a. Edmund played a nasty trick. He told Susan and Peter that Lucy was just pretending about a country in the wardrobe. He snickered and laughed at Lucy.

1. Edmund and Lucy were playing.
2. Edmund told lies about Lucy.
3. Edmund was in the wardrobe.
4. Edmund ate too much candy.

b. Lucy rushed out of the room crying. No one found her for a long time. She seemed very unhappy. Everyone suffered through an unpleasant evening.

1. Lucy liked to pretend.
2. The children played hide-and-seek.
3. Lucy was very unhappy.
4. Edmund was kind to Lucy.

(continued)

Getting the Main Idea

Back of This Side of the Door

c.   Susan and Peter were very concerned about Lucy. They began to think she was out of her mind. They stood in the hall and talked about her wild story. The next day, they spoke to the Professor.

1. Susan and Peter were worried about Lucy.
2. The Professor was always in his study.
3. Susan and Peter talked all night.
4. Lucy and the Professor were good friends.

---

d.   The Professor's old house was mentioned in guide books and history books. Many people came to visit the house. Mrs. Macready took the sightseers around the house, showing the various rooms.

1. The house had many rooms.
2. Mrs. Macready worked for the Professor.
3. Tourists bothered the Professor.
4. The Professor's house was very famous.

Remembering Details

The following questions are about some of the characters and events in the book. Write the answers on the lines after the questions. Be sure to use complete sentences.

. What did Susan suggest the children do to keep warm? _____

_____

. What did Edmund say that made the others realize he had been in Narnia before?

_____

. Who did Peter think should be the leader through the woods? _____

_____

. Whom did Lucy want to visit? _____

_____

. What was wrong with the cave? _____

_____

. What had happened to the Faun? _____

_____

. Why was the Faun taken away? _____

_____

. What kind of bird did the children follow? _____

_____

Into the Forest

Determining Fact and Opinion

Some of the following sentences are statements of fact. Some are statements of opinion. In the blank before each sentence, write the letter *F* if that sentence is a statement of fact. Write *O* if that sentence is a statement of opinion.

Example: ___*F*___ The children hid in the wardrobe.

_____ 1. The wardrobe smelled awful.

_____ 2. Lucy had a wild imagination.

_____ 3. The children wore fur coats.

_____ 4. A fur coat is the best protection against the cold.

_____ 5. A hike through a dark woods is very exciting.

_____ 6. The children walked through the forest.

_____ 7. The snowstorm would begin before nightfall.

_____ 8. Lucy deserved to be the leader.

_____ 9. Clouds hung in the sky overhead.

_____ 10. The children walked to Mr. Tumnus' cave.

(continued)

Determining Fact and Opinion

Into the Forest

_____ 11. Only the children could help Mr. Tumnus.

_____ 12. Mr. Tumnus was not at home.

_____ 13. The White Witch was wicked and hateful.

_____ 14. The picture of Mr. Tumnus' father had been cut.

_____ 15. A piece of paper was nailed to the cave floor.

_____ 16. Narnia was not a pleasant place.

_____ 17. The children did not have any food with them.

_____ 18. Always trust robins to lead the way.

_____ 19. The children followed the robin.

_____ 20. The robin will lead the children into a trap.

A Day with the Beavers

Drawing Conclusions

In each of the following paragraphs, an item is described but not named. Read each paragraph and decide what is being described. Write your answers on the blank after each question.

1. They saw him hiding behind a tree. He motioned for the children to follow him. Putting a paw to his furry, whiskered face, he whispered, "Hush!" Peter knew what kind of animal it was by the broad, flat tail.

    What kind of animal was it? _____

2. The animal held out the small white cloth. Lucy recognized it immediately. She had given it to Mr. Tumnus to wipe away his tears. Now this animal had it as a token of friendship.

    What was the cloth? _____

3. The animal led the children to a spot where four objects grew. The objects stood so close together that their boughs met and sheltered the earth below from snow. The animal whispered because the tall objects always listened. Some would even betray the children to the evil queen.

    What were the objects? _____

(continued)

Drawing Conclusions

A Day with the Beavers

4. Beavers always build them. This one was built across a fairly large river. The beaver used many branches and twigs to build it. Susan complimented the beaver on his fine work.

   What had the beaver built? _____

5. The beaver hoped to catch some for supper. He walked across the ice on the pond and chopped open a small hole. He sat by the hole and grabbed some as they swam past.

   What did the beaver catch? _____

6. The beaver peered carefully out of it. It was a bit fogged over because of the warmth from the oven. He wiped a clear space on it. He could see that snow was gently falling outside.

   What was the beaver looking through? _____

A Day with the Beavers

Determining Cause and Effect

To determine a cause, ask "What is the reason?" To determine an effect, ask "What is the result?" Match the causes and effects below. Write the number of the cause in front of its effect.

Cause	Effect
1. The weather in Narnia was cold.	_____ The beaver whispered to the children.
2. The beaver had Lucy's handkerchief.	_____ The White Witch arrested him.
3. The trees always listened.	_____ Mr. Beaver chopped a hole in the ice.
4. They were not safe in the open.	_____ The children wore fur coats.
5. Mr. Tumnus was friendly to Lucy.	_____ No one could follow the children's tracks.
6. The path over the dam was covered with ice.	_____ The beaver led them to a dark spot in the woods.
7. There was only one chair in the beaver's house.	_____ The children knew it was a token of friendship.
8. The pond was frozen.	_____ They ate a hearty supper.
9. The children were hungry.	_____ The children sat on three-legged stools.
0. Snow was falling.	_____ They walked carefully so they would not slip.

Discovering Meaning Through Context

Read the following sentences. Three meanings are given for each italicized word. Use the context of the sentence to figure out which meaning is correct. Circle the correct meaning.

Example: The *prophecy* said two Sons of Adam and two Daughters of Eve would sit on the thrones.

    poem   (prediction)   book

. Peter proposed several *stratagems* to free the Faun.

    riddles   plans   problems

. Mr. Beaver meant no *offense* to the children when he made a comment about humans.

    offering   surprise   insult

. The White Witch's *reign* would end when the thrones at Cair Paravel were filled.

    rule   life   fight

. Mr. Beaver grew silent after he made his *remark* about the Witch.

    joke   comment   picture

. Susan *despaired* of ever finding her lost brother.

    lost hope   destroyed   grew tired

(continued)

Discovering Meaning
Through Context

What Happened After Dinner

6. The snow *muffled* the children's voices as they yelled for Edmund.

   twisted   moved   softened

7. The Witch used Edmund as *bait* to catch the rest of the children.

   fish   a lure   messenger

8. Reindeer pulled the Witch's *sledge* through the snow.

   sled   stone   statue

9. Edmund *betrayed* his brother and sisters when he went to the Witch.

   forgave   helped   double-crossed

10. Mr. Beaver *shuddered* at the thought of being turned into stone.

    cried   trembled   fainted

THE LION, THE WITCH AND THE WARDROBE

What Happened After Dinner

Remembering Details

To work the puzzle, use the words that complete the sentences below.

Across

4. The girls were called ____ of Eve.
9. The Witch turned people into ____ made of stone.
11. The Witch called herself a ____ .
13. ____ was the name of the country inside the wardrobe.
16. The Witch traveled by ____ .
18. The Witch did not have a drop of ____ blood in her.

Down

1. The boys were called Sons of ____.
2. ____ was the younger girl.
3. The queen sat on a ____ .
5. ____ was the younger brother.
6. ____ was the older sister.
7. Mrs. ____ cooked a fish supper.
8. Mr. ____ was a Faun.
10. A soft, new ____ fell in the woods.
12. Four thrones sat in ____ Paravel.
14. The lion's name was ____ .
15. ____ was the older brother.
17. Mr. Beaver built a ____ .

Remembering Details

The following questions are about some of the characters and events in the book. Write the answers on the lines after the questions. Be sure to use complete sentences.

1. What did Edmund wish he could eat? _____

_____

2. What had Edmund already done by the time Mr. Beaver spoke about the Witch?

_____

3. What is the first thing Edmund would do if he were king? _____

_____

4. What animal did Edmund first see inside the gate at the queen's castle? _____

_____

5. Why did the animal remain motionless? _____

_____

6. What did Edmund want to tell the Witch? _____

_____

Understanding Special Meanings

Read the following sentences. Explain in your own words the meaning of the italicized word or group of words. Write your response on the line below each sentence.

Example: Peter said Edmund was *a beast* to Lucy.

_____ *mean* _____

1. Edmund wanted to *pay Peter back* for what he said.

_____

2. Edmund did not want his brother and sisters *at his same level.*

_____

3. With the full moon shining, the night *seemed like day.*

_____

4. A wind *sprang up* and the air became very cold.

_____

(continued)

Understanding
Special Meanings

In the Witch's House

5. The long pointed spires looked *like needles*.

   _____

6. The castle towers were *like huge dunce's caps*.

   _____

7. The sight nearly *made his heart stop beating*.

   _____

8. Edmund became warm *right down to his toes*.

   _____

9. The huge stone giant was *like a tree*.

   _____

Name _____

THE LION, THE WITCH AND THE WARDROBE

The Spell Begins to Break

Matching Synonyms

A synonym is a word having the same or nearly the same meaning as another word. Choose a synonym for each word in the Word List. Write the synonym on the blank.

Word List		Synonym
Example: sack	*bag*	larger
1. load	_____	final
2. hurry	_____	trail
3. steal	_____	shake
4. start	_____	rush
5. journey	_____	disappear
6. last	_____	~~bag~~
7. path	_____	evil
8. tired	_____	rob
9. look	_____	burden
10. vanish	_____	weary
11. bad	_____	speak
12. bigger	_____	trip
13. shiver	_____	gaze
14. present	_____	gift
15. talk	_____	begin

© 1985 The Perfection Form Company

The Spell Begins to Break

Matching Antonyms

An antonym is a word which means the opposite or nearly the opposite of another word. Choose an antonym for each word in the Word List. Write the antonym on the blank.

Word List		Antonym
Example: right	*wrong*	end
1. lead	_____	start
2. all	_____	fix
3. finish	_____	same
4. clean	_____	noisy
5. before	_____	after
6. true	_____	bottom
7. break	_____	ask
8. begin	_____	light
9. dark	_____	narrow
10. wide	_____	follow
11. top	_____	early
12. late	_____	dirty
13. answer	_____	none
14. different	_____	false
15. silent	_____	~~wrong~~

THE LION, THE WITCH AND THE WARDROBE

Aslan is Nearer

Determining Alphabetical Order

Words are listed in a dictionary in alphabetical order. Number the six words in each list below to show the order in which they would appear in a dictionary. Write *1* on the blank before the word that comes first alphabetically, and so on.

Example:

_6_ dwarf
_2_ courage
_4_ delight
_1_ change
_5_ disappoint
_3_ creature

A.
_____ fool
_____ faint
_____ food
_____ falling
_____ enormous
_____ floor

B.
_____ beaver
_____ brat
_____ as
_____ began
_____ bread
_____ bring

C.
_____ kill
_____ it
_____ like
_____ kind
_____ last
_____ little

D.
_____ pudding
_____ on
_____ now
_____ party
_____ old
_____ one

E.
_____ glad
_____ have
_____ had
_____ gallop
_____ glass
_____ he

F.
_____ time
_____ warmer
_____ were
_____ there
_____ very
_____ wet

G.
_____ merry
_____ moment
_____ meaning
_____ majesty
_____ muddy
_____ must

H.
_____ quite
_____ stop
_____ sledge
_____ quarter
_____ reason
_____ risen

85 The Perfection Form Company

Aslan is Nearer

Determining Alphabetical Order

Most of the words in the list below are in alphabetical order. However, some of the words have either jumped ahead or fallen back. Cross out the words that are too far ahead or too far back. The remaining words will then be in alphabetical order. Complete the Word-Search Puzzle by hunting down the correctly alphabetized words.

black
primroses
blue
curse
spring
delicious
fog
glades
gold
alive
green
hole
thaw
larch
merry
purple
delicate
robes
silver
forth
snow
transparent
white
either
winter

Word-Search Puzzle

```
A  T  R  A  N  S  P  A  R  E  N  T
B  D  C  D  M  R  E  V  L  I  S  I
K  C  A  L  B  E  E  L  K  J  M  P
S  P  O  O  L  N  R  F  G  H  R  U
U  N  Q  G  U  R  S  R  T  U  E  R
O  Y  O  S  E  W  X  S  Y  V  T  P
I  F  Z  W  E  A  E  E  B  C  N  L
C  U  R  S  E  H  F  B  D  E  I  E
I  K  A  U  S  I  C  O  E  G  W  H
L  T  W  L  J  N  O  R  P  L  Y  X
E  S  E  D  A  L  G  Q  A  R  O  B
D  V  Z  M  W  H  I  T  E  L  C  H
```

THE LION, THE WITCH AND THE WARDROBE

Peter's First Battle

Using a Pronunciation Key

Use the key at the bottom of the page to help pronounce the respelled words. Write the word correctly spelled on the line beside the Respelled Word. Use the Word List to help figure out the Respelled Word.

Respelled Word		Word List
Example: (kur′ ənt)	*currant*	heavy
1. (hōl)	_____	breeze
2. (klīm)	_____	pavilion
3. (skēm)	_____	straighten
4. (brēz)	_____	expression
5. (hwis′ pər)	_____	castle
6. (pə vil′ yən)	_____	whole
7. (hev′ ē)	_____	creature
8. (ri flek′ shən)	_____	hour
9. (strāt′ ən)	_____	reflection
10. (our)	_____	scheme
11. (vel′ vit)	_____	whisper
12. (krē′ chə)	_____	~~currant~~
13. (kas′ ′l)	_____	velvet
14. (ik spresh′ ən)	_____	climb

pat/ cāke/ cär/ pet/ mē/ it/ nīce/ pot/ cōld/ nôrth/
book/ fo͞ol/ boil/ out/ cup/ mūle/ burn/ sing/ thin/
*th*is/ hw in **wh**ite/ zh in pleasure/ ə in about
The ′ mark indicates an accented syllable.

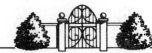

THE LION, THE WITCH AND THE WARDROBE

Using Guide Words

At the top of each dictionary page are guide words. These words are the first and last words on a dictionary page. The other words on the page fall in alphabetical order between the guide words.

Put the boxed words below in alphabetical order under the correct guide words. One has been done for you.

masses	closing	hour
lovely	sunlight	~~awkward~~
dense	moss	smell
kingfisher	longer	magic
they	far	feet
elms	overhead	hilltop

act—fin	**final—march**	**mare—tongue**
1. *awkward*	1. _____	1. _____
2. _____	2. _____	2. _____
3. _____	3. _____	3. _____
4. _____	4. _____	4. _____
5. _____	5. _____	5. _____
6. _____	6. _____	6. _____

Deep Magic from the Dawn of Time

Choosing Correct Meanings

The italicized word in each of the sentences below has several meanings. The meanings are listed in the Glossary. Decide which meaning the word has in the sentence. Then write the number of your choice on the blank.

Glossary

back   1. the part of the body behind the chest   2. to help   3. to move backward
      4. to return

bound   1. tied; fastened   2. certain   3. obligated   4. to leap

face   1. the front of the head   2. front part of something   3. turn the face toward
      4. to meet with courage

present   1. to introduce one person to another   2. to give   3. to display

side   1. the right or left part of a person's body   2. one of two or more opposing groups

still   1. without movement   2. silent   3. at this time; as before

Example: ____/____ Edmund lay on his *back*.

_____ 1. The Witch *still* had her wand.

_____ 2. The Dwarf kicked Edmund in the *side*.

_____ 3. Edmund was *bound* to a tree.

_____ 4. He *presented* himself to the Witch.

_____ 5. Edmund sat *still* by the tree, too tired to move.

(continued)

Choosing Correct Meanings

Deep Magic from the Dawn of Time

_____ 6. The Witch's *face* was dead-white.

_____ 7. Fenris Ulf *bounded* toward the Witch.

_____ 8. He came *back* to the Witch.

_____ 9. Edmund solemnly *presented* his hand to his brother and sisters.

_____ 10. Mr. Beaver *backed* away.

_____ 11. The two *sides* held a meeting.

_____ 12. Lucy put her hand on Aslan's *back*.

_____ 13. Aslan turned to *face* the Witch.

_____ 14. Everyone was *still* while Aslan and the Witch talked.

_____ 15. Aslan was *bound* to beat the Witch.

THE LION, THE WITCH AND THE WARDROBE

Deep Magic from the Dawn of Time

Making an Outline

Read the article below. Think about the topics and subtopics of each paragraph. Use the Word List provided to outline the article. The topics should come after the numerals. The subtopics come after the capital letters. List the topics and subtopics in the order the items fall in the article.

Part of the outline has been done for you. Be sure to capitalize the first letter of the topics and subtopics.

Lions

The lion is the largest animal in the cat family. The male usually weighs about 400 pounds and is around nine feet long. Lions stand about four feet tall at the shoulder. They have very strong forelegs and sharp claws.

A lion has thirty teeth. Some of the teeth serve special purposes. The lion's pointed teeth hold and kill prey and help tear meat. Lions use their cheek teeth to bite through tough skin and to cut the tendons of prey.

Lions prefer large prey like zebras or antelopes. They also eat buffalos, warthogs, and deer.

(continued)

Making an Outline

Deep Magic from the Dawn of Time

_____ *Lions* _____

I. *Lion's body* _____

    A. _____

    B. _____

    C. _____

    D. _____

    E. _____

II. _____

    A. *Hold prey* _____

    B. _____

    C. _____

    D. _____

    E. _____

III. _____

    A. _____

    B. *Antelope* _____

    C. _____

    D. _____

    E. _____

Word List

400 pounds

Buffalos

Kill prey

~~Lions~~

Lion's teeth

~~Lion's body~~

Warthogs

Zebras

Bite skin

Nine feet long

Strong forelegs

~~Antelopes~~

Lion's food

Cut tendons

~~Hold prey~~

Sharp claws

Deer

Four feet tall

Tear meat

The Triumph of the Witch

Finding Facts in the Encyclopedia

A sample encyclopedia set is drawn below. Imagine that you need these volumes of the encyclopedia to respond to the questions below. Circle the word or words in each question that might help you find the answers.

Use the circled words to decide which volume or volumes you will need to answer each question. Write the volume number or numbers on the blank.

A	B	C-Ch	Ci-Cz	D	E	F	G	H	I	J-K	L	M	N-O	P	Q-R	S-Sn	So-Sz	T	U-V	W X YZ
1	2	3	4	5	6	7	8	9	10	11	12	13	14	15	16	17	18	19	20	21

Example: _____12_____ What color is a (lion)'s coat?

_____ 1. What does a castle look like?

_____ 2. Where do most lions live?

_____ 3. What is white magic?

_____ 4. What is witchcraft?

_____ 5. What does a wolf look like?

_____ 6. What is a centaur?

_____ 7. How many kinds of swords are there?

_____ 8. What food does a beaver eat?

_____ 9. What is a reindeer?

_____ 10. What is a ford?

Creating a Character

Imagine you have visited Narnia. You are being interviewed by a newspaper reporter. Write your responses to the reporter's questions on the lines provided. Be sure to use complete sentences.

Reporter: How did you discover Narnia?

Visitor: _____

_____

Reporter: What unusual things did you see in Narnia?

Visitor: _____

_____

Reporter: What did you like most about Narnia?

Visitor: _____

_____

Reporter: What did you like least about Narnia?

Visitor: _____

_____

Reporter: Would you like to live in Narnia? Why or why not?

Visitor: _____

_____

Deeper Magic from *Before* the Dawn of Time

Creating a Picture

Draw one of the scenes the author describes in "Deeper Magic from *Before* the Dawn of Time." Then write your own description of what you have drawn. Be sure to use complete sentences.

_____

_____

What Happened About the Statues

Connecting Words

Look at the three words in each set below. Combine the words to form a sentence that expresses a complete thought. Write the sentence on the line after each group of words.

Example: stone/statues/museum *Stone statues surrounded the museum*

1. lion/fur/golden _____

2. witch/curse/evil _____

3. battle/enemy/forest _____

4. creatures/horrible/shouts _____

5. bird/tree/chirped _____

6. dark/castle/gate _____

7. moon/brightly/evening _____

8. cold/snow/shivered _____

9. explore/strange/woods _____

10. whisper/hide/trees _____

11. house/old/secret _____

12. cried/unhappy/death _____

13. clouds/sky/dark _____

14. strong/giant/kind _____

15. giant/house/horrible _____

THE LION, THE WITCH AND THE WARDROBE

What Happened About the Statues

Writing a Journal Sample

Imagine that you are one of the characters in the book. In the sample journal below, describe one of these events from your character's viewpoint: the awakening of the statues, the ransacking of the Witch's castle, or the battle against the Witch. Be sure to use complete sentences.

Character _____

THE LION, THE WITCH AND THE WARDROBE

Using Descriptive Words

List seven words that can be used to describe each of the italicized words below. Be creative. Write your words on the blanks.

Example: *ghost*

1. *pale*
2. *spooky*
3. *mischievous*
4. *floating*
5. *mysterious*
6. *shimmering*
7. *friendly*

A. *lion*

1. _____
2. _____
3. _____
4. _____
5. _____
6. _____
7. _____

B. *witch*

1. _____
2. _____
3. _____
4. _____
5. _____
6. _____
7. _____

C. *castle*

1. _____
2. _____
3. _____
4. _____
5. _____
6. _____
7. _____

D. *forest*

1. _____
2. _____
3. _____
4. _____
5. _____
6. _____
7. _____

THE LION, THE WITCH AND THE WARDROBE

Describing Feelings

A person does not always express feelings directly in words. Sometimes feelings are shown through other clues as well. Each of the sentences below provides clues to the feelings of a character in the book. The name of that character is italicized. First study the clues, then choose the word from the box that best describes the character's feelings. Write that word on the blank in front of the sentence.

worried	excited	curious	afraid	contented
relieved	angry	unhappy	amused	amazed

_____ 1. After a tasty tea, *Lucy* lazily leaned back in her chair and listened to Mr. Tumnus play his flute.

_____ 2. *Susan* laughed, "Lucy, you goose, no one could believe there's a country inside the wardrobe."

_____ 3. *Peter* breathed easier when the Professor said Lucy was not mad.

_____ 4. *Lucy* shouted and clapped her hands when she saw that Edmund was in Narnia, too.

_____ 5. *Lucy* burst into tears.

_____ 6. *Peter* wondered who Aslan was.

_____ 7. "We must find Edmund! Where can he possibly be?" *Susan* cried.

_____ 8. *Peter's* mouth dropped open when Mr. Beaver said Edmund had gone to the White Witch.

_____ 9. "Don't ever mention that name again!" the *Witch* screamed. "If you do, I'll have your head!"

_____ 10. *Lucy* trembled when she realized the White Witch would soon be after them.

Explaining Feelings

The questions below ask you to describe the feelings you had as you read the book. Read each question carefully. Write your response on the lines provided. Explain why you felt the way you did. Be sure to use complete sentences.

. How did you feel when no one believed Lucy's story about Narnia?

_____

_____

_____

. How did you feel when Edmund left the beavers' home and went to the Witch?

_____

_____

_____

How did you feel when the Witch was unkind to Edmund?

_____

_____

_____

(continued)

Explaining Feelings

4. How did you feel when the Witch killed Aslan?

_____

_____

_____

5. How did you feel when Aslan brought the statues back to life?

_____

_____

_____

6. How did you feel when the children became kings and queens of Narnia?

_____

_____

_____

7. How did you feel when the children found themselves back home after living fo
so many years in Narnia?

_____

_____

_____

Optional Spelling and Vocabulary Lists

Below are six word lists from the book. The lists can be used as spelling or vocabulary words.

Chapters 1—3

professor	empty
housekeeper	eagles
amount	badgers
several	parcels
further	castle
extremely	vanish
umbrella	hoax
gracious	spies
introduce	eternal
caverns	majesty

Chapters 4—6

confused	copper
patience	contain
delight	secret
diamond	nasty
direction	success
separate	liar
superior	logic
difference	beasts
savagely	passage
whispers	reliable

Chapters 7—9

nervous	flown
actually	beaver
curious	risk
instantly	floated
expression	eager
spectacles	cruel
ventured	fierce
slippery	dwarf
decent	miserable
prophecy	vanished

Optional Spelling
and Vocabulary Lists

Chapters 10—12

journey	crock
solemn	drawer
scrambled	delay
sandwiches	sledge
repulsive	shield
announced	gallop
enormous	terror
squirrel	curse
creatures	reindeer
schemes	pavilion

Chapters 13—15

rescued	fir
summon	proper
captain	throne
escaped	victim
messenger	dispute
leopards	queen
traitor	savage
wondered	roar
shallow	promise
soldier	permission

Chapters 16—17

joyously	museum
concealed	yawn
sparkling	evil
companions	clever
managed	proper
presence	statue
rejoicing	stout
ordinary	rough
liberated	warrior
adventure	deafening

Supplementary Activities

Below is a list of ideas that could be used as supplementary or culminating activities.

I. Oral reading

    A. To the entire class

    B. To each other

    C. To the teacher

    D. To a tape recorder

II. Group discussions

    A. Author's writing style

    B. Ideas gained from the book

    C. Parts of the book

        1. Most important

        2. Most frightening

        3. Most amusing

        4. Most saddening

        5. Most exciting

        6. Most liked

    D. Characters

        1. Did the characters seem real?

        2. What was the most admirable trait of each character?

        3. What was the least admirable trait of each character?

        4. Which character was the student's favorite? Why?

        5. List questions to ask each character.

Supplementary Activities

III. Spelling bee using words from the book

IV. Role play situations from the book

V. Artistic creations

   A. Murals

   B. Dioramas

   C. Book jackets

   D. Posters

   E. Puppets

   F. Poetry

   G. Costumes

   H. Portraits

   I. Mobiles

   J. Songs

   K. Newspaper headlines, articles, and drawings

VI. Research

   A. Lion

   B. Witch

   C. Dwarf

   D. Faun or unicorn

   E. Wolf, beaver, or reindeer

   F. Castle

VII. Read other books by the same author

Response Key

WORD ATTACK SKILLS

Changing Short Vowels (page 7)

1. ten; 2. big; 3. odd; 4. bed; 5. foxes; 6. down; 7. shut; 8. smell; 9. tips; 10. fall; 11. back; 12. lamp; 13. dropped; 14. held; 15. stopped.

Supplying Long Vowels (page 8)

1. wife; 2. face; 3. stream; 4. huge; 5. coats; 6. easy; 7. rain; 8. cold; 9. light; 10. liked; 11. eagles; 12. strange; 13. white; 14. snow; 15. waist.

Making Compounds (page 9)

1. summertime; 2. mantelpiece; 3. bedroom; 4. bookshelf; 5. teakettle; 6. daylight; 7. something; 8. midnight; 9. wardrobe; 10. hallway.

Finding Base Words (page 11)

1. puzzle; 2. east; 3. country; 4. delight; 5. understand; 6. sudden; 7. set; 8. live; 9. gloom; 10. wonder; 11. shake; 12. sorrow; 13. cover; 14. mere; 15. begin; 16. take; 17. beauty; 18. present; 19. fright; 20. sob.

Listening for Syllables (page 12)

1. 2; 2. 2; 3. 4; 4. 2; 5. 4; 6. 3; 7. 1; 8. 4; 9. 1; 10. 3; 11. 2; 12. 2; 13. 1; 14. 3; 15. 2; 16. 3; 17. 2; 18. 2; 19. 1; 20. 2; 21. 3; 22. 2; 23. 3; 24. 2; 25. 3; 26. 3; 27. 3; 28. 2; 29. 1; 30. 2.

COMPREHENSION SKILLS

Classifying Word Groups (page 13)

1. when; 2. how; 3. where; 4. how; 5. where; 6. where; 7. when; 8. where; 9. how; 10. where; 11. when; 12. where; 13. how; 14. when; 15. how; 16. where; 17. where; 18. where; 19. how; 20. how.

Classifying Words (page 15)

1. first; 2. full; 3. door; 4. rock; 5. Narnia; 6. Queen; 7. pie; 8. ahead; 9. nest; 10. house; 11. light; 12. notice; 13. clouds; 14. golden; 15. fur; 16. walk 17. sunrise; 18. tassel; 19. shadow; 20. red.

Following Directions (page 16)
1. woods; 2. castle; 3. pond; 4. bushes; 5. bridge; 6. hill; 7. moat bridge; 8. ruins; 9. lamp-post.

Remembering Details (page 17)
1. The Queen put a fur mantle around Edmund. 2. There was a hot drink in the jewelled cup. 3. The Queen asked Edmund to bring his brother and sisters to her. 4. The Queen told Edmund he would become a prince and then a king. 5. Edmund was to bring his brother and sisters to the Queen's house. 6. Lucy had lunch with Mr. Tumnus, the Faun. 7. The White Witch called herself the Queen of Narnia. 8. Edmund felt uncomfortable because he had eaten too many sweets.

Sequencing Events (page 18)
3, 6, 9, 1, 4, 7, 2, 5, 8.

Getting the Main Idea (page 19)
a. Edmund told lies about Lucy. b. Lucy was very unhappy. c. Susan and Peter were worried about Lucy. d. The Professor's house was very famous.

Remembering Details (page 21)
1. Susan suggested that the children wear fur coats from the wardrobe. 2. Edmund said they should look for the lamp-post. 3. Peter thought Lucy should be the leader. 4. Lucy wanted to visit Mr. Tumnus. 5. No one was in the cave and everything was broken. 6. Mr. Tumnus, the Faun, had been arrested. 7. He had been taken away for hiding Lucy from the Witch. 8. The children followed a robin.

Determining Fact and Opinion (page 23)
1. O; 2. O; 3. F; 4. O; 5. O; 6. F; 7. O; 8. O; 9. F; 10. F; 11. O; 12. F; 13. O; 14. F; 15. F; 16. O; 17. F; 18. O; 19. F; 20. O.

Drawing Conclusions (page 25)
1. beaver; 2. handkerchief; 3. trees; 4. dam; 5. fish; 6. window.

Determining Cause and Effect (page 27)
3, 5, 8, 1, 10, 4, 2, 9, 7, 6.

iscovering Meaning Through Context (page 29)

plans; 2. insult; 3. rule; 4. comment; 5. lost hope; 6. softened; 7. a lure; 8. sled; double-crossed; 10. trembled.

emembering Details (page 31)

A L T
DAUGHTERS B
A C R D u E T
M Y O M STATUES
N u A V m N
QUEEN N E N O
C D R u W
NARNIA P S
I SLEDGE
R O L T
A A E
HUMAN R

membering Details (page 32)

Edmund wanted to eat Turkish Delight. 2. Edmund had already left the Beavers' me and gone out into the snow. 3. Edmund said the first thing he would do is make cent roads. 4. Edmund saw a lion. 5. The lion did not move because it was made stone. 6. He wanted to tell the Witch that his brother and sisters were at the Beavers' use.

derstanding Special Meanings (page 33)

get revenge; 2. to have equal power; 3. as bright as day; 4. suddenly blew; 5. sharp d thin; 6. in the shape of cones; 7. scared him to death; 8. all over his body; 9. tall d immovable.

tching Synonyms (page 35)

burden; 2. rush; 3. rob; 4. begin; 5. trip; 6. final; 7. trail; 8. weary; 9. gaze; disappear; 11. evil; 12. larger; 13. shake; 14. gift; 15. speak.

tching Antonyms (page 36)

follow; 2. none; 3. start; 4. dirty; 5. after; 6. false; 7. fix; 8. end; 9. light; 10. narrow; bottom; 12. early; 13. ask; 14. same; 15. noisy.

STUDY SKILLS

Determining Alphabetical Order (page 37)
A. 6, 2, 5, 3, 1, 4;
B. 2, 4, 1, 3, 5, 6;
C. 2, 1, 5, 3, 4, 6;
D. 6, 3, 1, 5, 2, 4;
E. 2, 5, 4, 1, 3, 6;
F. 2, 4, 5, 1, 3, 6;
G. 3, 4, 2, 1, 5, 6;
H. 2, 6, 5, 1, 3, 4.

Determining Alphabetical Order (page 38)

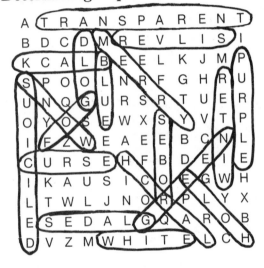

Words crossed out: primroses, spring, alive, thaw, delicate, forth, either

Using a Pronunciation Key (page 39)
1. whole; 2. climb; 3. scheme; 4. breeze; 5. whisper; 6. pavilion; 7. heavy; 8. reflection; 9. straighten; 10. hour; 11. velvet; 12. creature; 13. castle; 14. expression.

Using Guide Words (page 40)

act—fin	final—march	mare—tongue
1. awkward	1. hilltop	1. masses
2. closing	2. hour	2. moss
3. dense	3. kingfisher	3. overhead
4. elms	4. longer	4. smell
5. far	5. lovely	5. sunlight
6. feet	6. magic	6. they

Choosing Correct Meanings (page 41)
1. 3; 2. 1; 3. 1; 4. 1; 5. 1; 6. 1; 7. 4; 8. 4; 9. 2; 10. 3; 11. 2; 12. 1; 13. 3; 14. 2; 15. 2.

Making an Outline (page 43)
Lions

    I. Lion's body
      A. 400 pounds
      B. Nine feet long
      C. Four feet tall
      D. Strong forelegs
      E. Sharp claws

    II. Lion's teeth
      A. Hold prey
      B. Kill prey
      C. Tear meat
      D. Bite skin
      E. Cut tendons

    III. Lion's food
      A. Zebras
      B. Antelopes
      C. Buffalos
      D. Warthogs
      E. Deer

Finding Facts in the Encyclopedia (page 45)
1. 3, castle; 2. 12, lions; 3. 13, magic; 4. 21, witchcraft; 5. 21, wolf; 6. 3, centaur; 7. 18, swords; 8. 2, beaver; 9. 16, reindeer; 10. 7, ford.

CREATIVE SKILLS

Creating a Character (page 46)
Responses will vary.

Creating a Picture (page 47)
Responses and pictures will vary.

Connecting Words (page 48)
Responses will vary.

Writing a Journal Sample (page 49)
Responses will vary.

Using Descriptive Words (page 50)
Responses will vary.

Describing Feelings (page 51)
1. contented; 2. amused; 3. relieved; 4. excited; 5. unhappy; 6. curious; 7. worried; 8. amazed; 9. angry; 10. afraid.

Explaining Feelings (page 53)
Responses will vary.